Secrets From

The World's Most Productive

Nurse Practitioner

Secrets From The World's Most Productive Nurse Practitioner by Jessica Reeves

Published by Our Publishing
67 Winter Street, Keene, NH 03431

For permissions contact: ourpublishing@gmail.com

Cover by Jessica Reeves.

ISBN: 978-0-57888-936-8

Table of Contents

Dedication

To **The World's Most Supportive Husband**, *Timothy.*

Thank you for always being on board with all of my

schemes, and for being my biggest cheerleader. I am a

lucky lady.

Author's Note

Hi!

I'm Jessica. I'm a Nurse Practitioner who got in trouble for my excellent time management skills.

I got dinged for leaving "early" (at 4:50PM) even though my visits were done, all of my charts were closed, and my inbox was empty. I would have thought this would be deserving of applause, but instead I got rewarded by getting an email with the dreaded "action plan" subject line and being told to ask my colleagues if they needed any help.

Really.

I have always had kind of a thing for time management. My friends will tell you that I am always the first to arrive to an event. My husband will tell you that I know exactly how long everything he does should take. My mother taught me that if you are not five minutes early, you are late. None of them are wrong.

I went to nursing school while I was working as a director at a nonprofit – commuting approximately 7500 miles in the process, and graduating magna cum laude. I was part of the founding team of a community radio station while working full time as a senior leader at a nonprofit responsible for a staff of 12. I got a Masters in public health from an Ivy League school while working in Connecticut during the week (as a *super* green Nurse Practitioner) and commuting home to New Hampshire on the weekends (approximately two and a half hours away).

I like to keep busy. But I also like the challenge of balancing multiple tasks – and winning.

What I consider to be one of my biggest
accomplishments is my track record of four consecutive
quarters of closing 97-100% of my charts the same day
(during a pandemic, no less), while leaving at (or before)
5:00PM—with an empty inbox.

After realizing that commuting to Connecticut
every week and home to New Hampshire every

weekend was not a good fit for me, I took a job in a very busy family medicine practice (once described, not incorrectly, as riding a carousel placed on a roller coaster). There was talk of mentoring new associate providers (Nurse Practitioners and Physician Assistants), as there was a relatively high attrition rate at the one-year mark. Unfortunately, the practice was *so* busy that this never came to pass – but the thought of being able to provide mentorship for new associate providers stuck with me and in part found its way to these pages.

If you are a newly graduated provider looking for ways to manage your time effectively, keep your head above water, and to be sure that you are walking into a job that is the right fit for you, this book is for you. If you are a not-so-new provider who does not have a role model or mentor to provide guidance, this book is for you. I hope it helps.

Chapter 1

Where It All Began

I started my career in healthcare as an EKG tech, which certainly gave me an appreciation for the importance of delivering on time no matter what. I worked in a 400-bed hospital with an attached outpatient clinic; there was a team of us during the day, but in the evenings and on the weekends, we worked alone. Funky rhythms and heart attacks don't know the difference between first shift and second shift, and they have no idea what a weekend is, so there were certainly times that I was stretched a little thin and had to HUSTLE (run from one end of the hospital to the other, pushing a heavy EKG cart – this was the late 90s, so think of a grocery cart with an old-school desktop computer attached). Thankfully, performing an EKG is relatively quick, but getting from point A to point B is often not.

Working as a secretary for a visiting nurse association built on this appreciation for time. I learned not only about managing my own time and tasks, but also about understanding and managing expectations of time, and how the pieces of the healthcare team fit together.

My department was the hospice arm of the organization, located in a rural area, with some patients as far as 45 minutes away from our office. I was the touchpoint; the calls came through me, the standing orders were sent and received by me, the notes were filed by me.

Much like the funky rhythms that would sometimes make their appearance while I was working alone as an EKG tech, hospice patients are on their own

timeline; there are some signs of approaching death,

but there are just as many times that nurses were taken

by surprise by a relatively sudden change in the

patient's condition (while they were miles away, of

course).

Being at the swirling center of this department

gave me a clear sense of the administrative demands of

a healthcare office, and it certainly informed my work

as a Nurse Practitioner by allowing me to appreciate

how the different parts of the team fit together. It's

tempting to think that your job (whatever it may be) is

the most stressful one of the team, or that your

department is the busiest or most put-upon

department in your organization. You may even be right

about that. Working as a secretary helped me to

understand that all jobs have their stressors and areas

for improvement – and to never take for granted that what you are experiencing is the most (or least) stressful thing going. Things are sooo much more subtle than that.

As you move through this book, you'll see that I advocate strongly for not only knowing yourself and how you work, but also for having a good understanding of the way the folks that you work with operate. Understanding (and appreciating) their challenges benefits you both – it deepens your working relationship and can help with little things like running on time and big things like not hating your job. It's an investment that pays off.

I have also supervised a staff of 12. Regardless of the setting or the individual players, in any workplace things don't always go right, and there is always something that can be improved. Speaking from my supervisory soapbox, when things don't go right or need improvement it is *immensely* easier to make informed decisions and operational changes when there is data present – not just perceptions or recollections, but actual evidence. Even better if it is evidence that was collected contemporaneously.

You will see in the following chapters some strategies for collecting and using this sort of data in your job; it will help you to understand yourself and is a great foundation for reflective practice. But it can also help to point to solutions when things aren't going right and need improving. It can make your job easier, can improve your satisfaction, and can make the job of leadership that much easier (which they should appreciate!). And when problems arise, if you are the only person who is bringing hard evidence to the table, the chances of your solution being the one that is

enacted are that much better.

While this book started as a book about time

management and how to get out of the office on time

all the time, there are some other helpful elements that

found their way to the pages. Things like questions that

you should ask during the interview/negotiation process

that will really help you to understand the job that you

are walking into; you know how to be a clinician, but

how much training did you receive on how to assess the

culture of the workplace to see if it's going to be the

right fit for you? Avoid costly (and time consuming, and

sometimes heart-wrenching) mistakes by asking the

RIGHT questions before you make a decision about a

job offer. You also set yourself apart from the pack

when interviewing for a competitive position (or in a

competitive market) by asking the right questions.

As you move through this book and learn about yourself, your workplace, and your colleagues, you will also learn some skills of reflective practice. Building your skills of self-reflection will improve you as a clinician, will help you to be a better team-mate, and a more satisfied employee.

Chapter 2

What Is Time?

Time is a non-renewable resource. Once passed, time is gone forever and can never be recovered. Shouldn't it be treated accordingly?

Your time is important. Your patients' time is important. It should be protected and respected. I will go even further and say that we have a virtual moral imperative to not waste our time or anyone else's.

If you feel the same, welcome. We'll talk about how to understand the way you use your time, how to identify areas for improvement, strategies for taking your time back, and how to negotiate for time in a new job.

You have invested a significant amount of time to become a provider. You deserve to be able to reap the rewards from this investment, not the least of which is to have a work-life harmony. You deserve more than going home from the clinic every night exhausted, late, with charts left to complete. You deserve to walk out of that clinic at the end of your day (or a time reasonably close to it), without anything hanging over your head and the freedom to focus on things that are not related to work.

We'll get you there.

Chapter 3

BEFORE You Take The Job

Whether you are starting your first job as a Nurse Practitioner or your fifth, there are several things that you can do in advance to get a head start on managing your time, improving your work life, and by extension your life-life. The best defense is a good offense – and bear in mind that you may be the only person who will guard your time like it is your most precious resource.

Interview Questions – And Why They Are Important

At the interview, ask questions to get a sense for how the practice or department functions overall. Not only will this impress the interviewer because unlike many candidates, you have actually prepared questions, it will give you a sense of what to expect if you accept this position.

- "How is the department staffed?"
  - This will give you a sense of how much support you would have in this position – but beware of too much support. The salary for those staff members is paid with your billable hours.
- "Are there rooming staff assigned to individual providers or do they work in a round-robin fashion?"
  - If this practice has rooming staff assigned to providers, ask to meet them; they will have a significant impact on your work life (and vice versa).

- "What is the ratio of rooming staff to providers?"
  - Think about it: if there are two staff rooming for one provider, they are bringing patients back twice as fast as you are seeing them. (I've been there; you will be slammed all day, every day.) If there is one staff member rooming for two providers, that is a pace that is geared to the provider and generally less stressful.
- "What are the credentials of the rooming staff – MA, LPN, RN?"
  - The question behind this question is whether these people will be working under their own license, or yours.

- "How does the staff support providers?"

  - In addition to rooming patients, are there phone nurses who will contact patients to give them results of labs, answer routine questions, triage incoming appointments?

  - If this practice does not have phone nurses, imagine (or better yet, ask) how appointments are triaged, or how results are delivered to patients. Will you be on the hook, in addition to other responsibilities?

- "Who reports to whom?"

  - Is there a leader on team who supervises the support staff?

o How does that leader interface with providers and other departments (if applicable)?

o Is there a leader on team who is the point person for providers?

o How does that person interface with support staff, their leadership, and other departments?

- You are trying to determine whether this person is an adequate advocate for providers. You could ask directly for examples of how this person has been an advocate for providers on the team.

- You also want to assess the
  relationship among leadership;
  does it appear harmonious,
  antagonistic, fractured?
- "How long are visits?"
  - Are all visits the same length, or are
    some visits longer?
  - Is extra time given for new patient
    visits, or visits requiring an interpreter?

Now, some questions for how the providers
work. Just like talking with patients, you are trying to
draw out information; avoid yes or no questions. If you
have the opportunity to talk with multiple providers,
even better – it could be illuminating to compare
divergent answers.

- "How often do providers stay late, on average?"

  o This will give you a read on the culture of the providers, and whether it matches your own approach and preferences. An answer that shocks you should be a red flag.

- "Do providers tend to work through their lunch breaks?"

  o If yes – doing what? Are they attending meetings, charting, or still in visits?

- "Do the providers in this practice tend to take charts home? If so, approximately how often?"

  o This could be you; do you like what you are hearing?

- "How much administrative time (AKA "admin time") are providers given each day/week?"

- "What happens when providers can't get their charts done in a given time period*?"
- "Do providers take vacations?"
  - o You might be surprised by the answer to this; if you are, then you know it was the right question to ask, and maybe not the right job for you.

Pay as much attention to how these questions are answered as the answers themselves. Do the responses appear to be candid or guarded? Is the person you are speaking with smirky or stressed – or perhaps even surprised that you are asking? How about their body language?

[*I worked for a clinic that would send an email out (sort of a naughty list) each week to all of the providers who had more than 10 open charts by the deadline. While the email (thankfully) did not go out to the ENTIRE medical staff, it did go out to everyone with too many open charts and their supervisors...and it spelled out exactly how many open charts they had. (Was I ever on this "naughty list"? No!)

I think this was supposed to be a motivator for providers to keep up with charting; it certainly motivated me to an extent. But ask yourself this: do you want to work for a clinic that uses negative tactics like this to keep providers productive, or would you rather work for a clinic that would identify people who were struggling and ask how they could help?]

So They Made You An Offer

When you get an offer, circle back to that admin time question. This can be a great negotiating point; if they don't have the flexibility on salary that you would like, you could ask for a certain amount of admin time to be booked into your schedule each week (or an increase to the amount) AND an increase to vacation time (which, technically, does not cost them anything, and is so vital to helping you recharge).

Having regularly held admin time in your schedule is *essential* to your work-life harmony and well-being. Adequate admin time allows you to catch up on charting, respond to patient messages, renew refills, complete peer reviews—and maintain your sanity. With an appropriate amount of admin time each week, you increase your chances of being able to complete your work AT work (shouldn't that be the goal?) and avoid burnout by knowing there is a light at the end of the tunnel when you are feeling overwhelmed.

The average amount of admin time that full time providers get each week varies widely; I have seen schemes with four hours of admin time weekly for providers who see at least 16 patients a day, four hours a week for non-paneled providers, and I have even seen providers get a full eight hours each week of admin time that was not required to be completed in the office – meaning that those providers were only in the office four days a week (!).

If you do ask for admin time (or an increased amount) in the negotiation process, and your new clinic agrees, make sure that whatever you agree upon is included in your contract (or elsewhere in writing if your new position does not have a contract).

Speaking Of Contracts

You probably don't need to have an attorney review your contract, though I have found that a lot of people feel better when they do. One of the most important things that you can screen the contract for yourself is a non-compete clause; if you are not sure whether there is anything that would amount to a non-compete clause, ask your prospective employer directly or have an attorney review the contract.

I am hopeful that non-competes will soon go the way of the dinosaur, but at present there are a number of contracts that still include them, and if you ask me they are poison. If you're not familiar, a non-compete clause is a fancy way of tying you to your job; they may specify that if you voluntarily leave your contracted position, you will not work for a competing organization within a certain geographic range (usually based on distance, like 60 miles—maybe even more in a rural area), or for a certain amount of time (sometimes *years*). This could also include opening your own practice, which is a growing trend among Nurse Practitioners.

Don't paint yourself into a corner with a noncompete clause! Look carefully at your contract for any language that would limit your options if you were to part ways with your employer. And remember – I am not a lawyer, and I have not played one on TV, so you should certainly consult with an actual attorney for specific questions—and legally-binding answers.

The Length of Visits

You should also circle back to the length of visits as part of your negotiation process. Take this opportunity to have specific language written into your contract (or elsewhere, if applicable) that you will have longer visits for new patients, annual physicals, and patients requiring interpreter services, for example. (If your new employer already does this – congratulations!)

A good rule of thumb is approximately 10 minutes per unrelated concern for an established patient. I have found a 25–35-minute visit to be fair for most visits, and either a double-length visit (50+ minutes) or extended visit (45 minutes if a typical visit is

25-35 minutes) for new patients, comprehensive physicals, or visits requiring an interpreter (which is essentially two visits in one and always take more time). Worker's compensation visits also deserve more time, due to the documentation burden.

Onboarding – And The Questions You Need to Ask

Before accepting an offer, ask about their process for onboarding. In our industry, this can vary widely with no apparent rhyme or reason.

- How much of an orientation to the organization and specific clinic do they provide?

- How much training time do they provide with their EMR (unless you have used the exact one before, there is going to be a learning curve), and who does this training? (Is it a staff member who is "good with computers" or someone who has had specific training from the EMR company?)

- Will you have an opportunity to shadow with any other departments during your orientation period?

- Will you have an opportunity to shadow other staff on the team, such as rooming staff or phone nurses? (**PRODUCTIVE TIP**: this is a great opportunity to see how the team functions and to build a good rapport with your new teammates. I have found that staff are extremely impressed when a provider wants to know what they do, how they do it, the challenges and rewards of their job, and how the different pieces fit and function together to form the team.)

- How many patients will you be expected to see – will you start immediately with a full schedule, or will you be ramped up over time as you adjust?

Here is an example of an onboarding schedule that I had, which I think was very fair:

- Two days of orientation to the organization (an affiliate of a large hospital system)
- Half day of training on EMR system with a dedicated trainer (not just a staff member) in a dedicated learning lab (not at your desk during lunch with a ton of interruptions)
- Shadowing opportunities in departments that I requested, ranging from a half day to three days (I spent time with orthopedics, dermatology, pediatrics, allergy)

34

- Gradual buildup of schedule over time, starting with one patient in the morning and one in the afternoon; this gave ample time to adjust to the EMR and charting (in all honesty, it was a bit too slow to start)

- Weekly addition of one patient to schedule each session (week 1: two patients per day; week 2: four patients per day; week 3: six patients per day, etc.)

Not So Fast

As you consider the offer that has been provided, complete a reflective journaling exercise to tap into your feelings about this potential workplace and position. (We will talk in more detail about developing an ongoing reflective practice in a later chapter.)

After your interview and/or after receiving an offer, set aside some time when you won't be interrupted (at least 20-30 minutes – this is important!). Gather your materials: notebook, pen, comfortable seat, beverage or snack. I highly recommend using pen and paper to complete this exercise as writing by hand can help to tap into our genuine, unedited thoughts more effectively than typing. Ask yourself the following questions, and write out your responses in your notebook:

- Did staff attitudes/behaviors appear to be in alignment with their responses to your questions? (Consider ALL staff with which you interacted.) Give examples.
- Did you notice any red flags? Give examples.

- What took you by surprise? Was it a good or

  bad surprise?

- Were there any gaps between what was said,

  and behaviors displayed? Give examples.

- What might you gain by accepting this position?

- What might you sacrifice by accepting this

  position?

Chapter 4

Once You Have Decided to Take The Job

You had the interview and impressed them; they had all the right answers to your questions, and they impressed you. They made an offer, you reflected, negotiated, and accepted, and now it is time to get to work. (Congratulations, by the way!)

Get to Know Your Relationship With Time

In order to effectively manage your time, you have to have a sense of what is actually happening with your time. Have you heard of PDSA cycles before? They are a management tool used to analyze a variety of problems; we see them used frequently in quality improvement. I love how elegantly simple, yet effective, they can be. **PDSA** stands for "**P**lan, **D**o, **S**tudy, **A**ct" and here is a quick version of how the elements are implemented:

- Describe the process being evaluated and devise a **PLAN** to address the problem
- **DO** what the plan says (follow it pretty exactly)
- **STUDY** the results of implementing the plan as described
  - make changes to the plan as a result of analyzing the results
- **ACT** on the updated plan

It is typical to go through several PDSA cycles while perfecting (or, more typically, standardizing) a process. I suggest you do the same to get a sense of how you use your time (check out the PDSA worksheet in the Appendix). There is not a precise endpoint for

PDSA cycles; it is generally advised to continue the process until reaching a point of "saturation," or until it seems the process cannot be further improved at that point in time.

Here's how you will use this process to understand your relationship with time: start by tracking what you do with your time, and then analyze that data to gain an understanding of where exactly all of your time is going (like a budget). There are time management tracker sheets in the Appendix; use these to track your time. You will notice that these time trackers cover 24 hours – your time at work and your time out of work. I recommend tracking an entire day as you are working to assess work-life harmony; you want to see where any spillover from your workday creeps into your personal time, and vice versa. Fill out these

sheets honestly, and you may be surprised by the
results.

Write down *everything* that you do; you don't
need to go into great detail (it would be fine to block
out several hours and just write "SLEEPING"), though
during your typical work hours you should write more
detailed notes (without using patient identifying
information). If you spent the morning seeing eight
patients, resulting labs, consulting with colleagues, and
reading emails, that all gets recorded. If you ran late
while seeing patients, even just one or two visits, that
gets written down, too.

Do this for a full work week, then set aside
some time on your first day off and review. Keep these
questions in mind as you review your results:

- What went right?
- What could have gone better?

- What did not go as expected?

- What do you need in order to get the
  results that you want?

When reviewing your results, keep an eye out for missed opportunities; if you did things a little differently, would you get big results? Would your work life be easier? Jot down some notes and some flexible strategies that you want to incorporate in the next week.

When the next week comes, repeat the process, incorporating any changes that you decided on after reviewing your results and reflecting. Repeat the process as many times as you need to until you feel that you have reached maximum improvement or a steady state.

Rule of thumb: most people will see improvement even after one or two PDSA cycles; it is not unusual to be very enlightened after studying your use of time, especially in such granular detail.

Hang onto these documents; if a time comes when you need to sit down with leadership and ask for more admin time or other things to help your job go more smoothly or your team to function more effectively, this is hard data that can be *very* helpful in backing up your case. And bonus points: it shows that you have the initiative and that you are reflective in your practice on many levels, including how you can improve your own performance. Look at you!

Getting Familiar With Your New Team

As you are getting to know your new team, an important part of managing your time will come from understanding your resources and the context in which they operate. You have worked on getting a deeper understanding of how you handle your time by tracking and analyzing your habits. Keep an eye on your new teammates; are there any potential time-drains that you may want to approach differently with time management in mind?

I had a colleague who was very knowledgeable and a great resource for curveball patients, but also extremely chatty. If I had all the time in the world, this would be great; I could learn a lot from him. But I usually didn't have a lot of time, so I had to learn how to use my time with him effectively. Presenting cases to him as "front-loaded" as possible so that once I was done presenting all he needed to do was give me a brief YES or NO answer was very, very helpful. Any chatting that occurred after that was at my discretion, and I could jump out of the conversation when I needed.

What happened when you asked in the interview about having the opportunity to shadow other staff members? This is such a great way to build rapport with your new colleagues and get a really good understanding of how the team functions. In my first week in a job in a large clinic, I was brought around and introduced to everyone; I lost count, but it was around 40 people. I barely remembered all of their names, much less how they fit together to form a team (note to self: next time, bring a small notebook and write it down). It took about a year before I really understood who did what, and where one job function picked up and another left off. How different would things have been if I had the opportunity to spend chunks of time with even a few of these staff members?

If you can spend some time following the medical assistants as they room patients (you don't need to spend all day, just follow them for a couple of patients), you will not only get a sense of what they are doing to prepare a patient to see a provider, but chances are really good that you will gain their respect – because you actually care. Knowing the challenges that they are facing, whether it is with individual patients or other resources, can present an opportunity for you to work with them toward creating a solution, or understanding when things do not go as planned.

How about sitting in with a phone nurse for half an hour? What kinds of calls do they get – and how do they handle them? How do they document, and what are their expectations after they have passed a message along? What resources do they use for triage? What makes their job hard, and what could make it easier? You might not be able to make the changes they need, but if you understand where they are coming from,

your job just got that much easier.

Is another provider willing to let you sit in with

them while they go through some results or close out a

few charts? Doing this will give you a chance to see the

EMR system up close and personal. Even better if you

can tag along on a patient visit or two; what better way

to get an idea of the patients of this practice and how

they tend to interface with the staff?

Can you observe while the secretaries check a

few patients in or out, and schedule a few

appointments? What resources do they use when it

comes to booking appointments? Do they have any

guidelines or algorithms or even a list of the providers'

preferences in booking appointments? Are they totally

overloaded with work? Are there things that they

anticipate from providers (such as guidance for booking

follow up appointments) that they aren't getting? Can you be part of the solution?

Know When to Hold 'Em, Known When to Fold 'Em

In your new position / new role, you will have to make choices. You can keep your internal customers (other staff, administration) happy; you can keep external customers (patients) happy; you can run on time. Choose two of the three – the reality is that it is not possible to successfully and consistently hit all three of these targets at the same time.

In my practice, I choose to keep internal customers happy and to run on time. My visits run consistently on time, and I leave the office on time every day with all of my charts closed, and I have a decent work-life harmony - but I have room for improvement with patient satisfaction scores. I wish it didn't have to be this way, but I recognize that it is not possible to keep all three of those balls in the air at the same time, and I am satisfied with my choices. Think through the context in which you will be (or are) practicing and choose your battles. You may find over time that your choices change but understanding your motivations for the choices that you have made is powerful and important.

It is typically easier to relax your boundaries after a while than it is to try to put boundaries in place when you have a mountain of charts and tasks in front of you. I suggest being conservative to start, and over time if you find that you have some room for flexibility and *want* to be more flexible with your boundaries, you can make that decision.

It is also important to recognize that some days are just not going to go smoothly. Give yourself a break when this happens and realize that there is a fair amount of stuff that goes on in *any* clinical practice that is firmly outside of your control; don't freak out too hard when this happens. Beating yourself up solves nothing; instead, find a moment to rapidly assess the situation, determine what (if anything) you have the power to do differently, and shift what you can.

Recognize that you may not be able to do anything other than cope in the short term – and that's okay! Your priority will be to get through it, and when the dust settles, reflect on whether there was anything that you could change to prevent the same thing from happening again. It may sound corny, but everything is a potential learning opportunity, given enough time.

Chapter 5

Charting

Now that you're on the job, there is a slew (some call it an avalanche) of tasks, requests, patient needs, lunch-and-learns, before work meetings, after work meetings, memos, and more coming at you from all angles without any end in sight. Time to get your arms around all of this.

Leave Work at Work

Remember when we talked about having boundaries? **RULE: Never take charting home with you. Ever.** If you do it more than once, it can seem "normal" or become a habit all too easily. "Oh, it's only two charts – it won't even take me that long," you say to yourself. But "only two charts" can easily turn into "only three charts" and then "only five charts," and the next thing you know it's a month later and you are charting at home at 10:00 PM.

When you take charting home, you are blurring the line between home and work. You are not respecting your work life by keeping it in its proper perspective; you are not respecting your home life when you let work responsibilities bleed over into your off hours. You are not respecting your friends and family by not being fully present in your off hours. You are not respecting yourself by keeping appropriate boundaries and allowing yourself an appropriate amount of time to recharge your batteries.

Raise Your Hand

If you can't be done for the day with 80% or more of your charts closed by 5:00PM (or within 30 minutes of the end of your last appointment) on most workdays, your clinic needs to know this, and you need to define and maintain your boundaries (or renew efforts to do this). If you have followed my advice so far, you should have an understanding of why you are not able to reach this milestone (between having tracked your time, completing PDSA cycles, and reflective journaling); review these materials and this insight when speaking with leadership about your needs.

Having actual data – as opposed to anecdotal evidence – that you can bring to support your requests should be helpful to all parties concerned. There is a chance that you are not the only person who is experiencing these symptoms; maybe the expectations need to be adjusted on the part of the clinic, the

patients, or you. Depending where in your career you

are, maybe the expectations placed on you by the clinic

are too stringent; would having a slot held in the

morning and the afternoon for a few weeks be enough

to help you adjust and get up to speed?

If you are having this conversation with your

leadership, bring ideas for solutions as well as the data

that you have collected regarding your performance.

This will position you as someone who is treating the

issue seriously (not someone who is chronically late

because they are posting their outfit of the day on

social media), and that you have high standards for

yourself.

My experience, both as an employee and as a

leader, is that people who come in with a clearly

identified problem and potential solution(s) are the

ones who are most motivated to do a great job – and as a leader, I have always been willing to do what I could to meet them halfway.

The Act, and Art, of Charting

Charting is the single activity that will take the most time of any clinician's schedule. Strangely, this is not a topic that is covered in depth in nursing or medical training, despite the fact that it is a universal challenge. The notes contained in charts are essentially currency in medicine; without a completed, coded, signed note, there is no bill—and no revenue for the organization. On the flip side, having your notes completed in a timely fashion on a regular basis means that you are doing your part to generate revenue predictably and reliably for the organization. It also means that all of the potential liabilities the organization may face from having a significant number of open notes is reduced where you are concerned. (Super star!)

I have never been a fan of charting in the room with the patient. I feel it is rude and can come across as treating the patient like a number instead of a person with a health concern or interest in maintaining their health. One of my other pet peeves with the practice of charting in the room is that in my case, it tends to make my visits run longer rather than saving me any time – and I can't have that!

I also find it challenging to enter orders while in the room with the patient. Depending on what you are ordering, it can be really easy to make a costly mistake; entering in the wrong dosage for a medication would be a biggie, but entering incorrect information in a PT referral that delays treatment is also bad. My experience is that patients don't discriminate what they are telling you when there are no distractions versus when you are trying to focus on the chart. I have had some real bombshells dropped on me while trying to enter a simple prescription for a Zpak - it's not an experience that I would like to repeat.

I do have colleagues who successfully chart in the room with the patient (usually just a part of the visit, like the chief complaint and subjective/objective findings, but it's still helpful to them in their time management). It can be done, but I think it depends on the user. It is certainly worth a (cautious) try and when successful can reduce the amount of paperwork left for you at the end of the visit.

If you want to see if charting in the room is beneficial for you, complete two PDSA cycles and evaluate. Chart in the room for every patient for a week, tracking your time for the day. At the end of the week, review and reflect, and look for opportunities for improvement; did you save as much time as you anticipated? Did this create more work for you in the long run? Were there any unexpected curveballs in approaching charting this way?

Refine your approach for the second week based on your reflections. Track your time again, and see where things land. Two PDSA cycles should be enough time to give you an answer about whether this is a strategy that you feel comfortable with and that truly saves you time. If it gets you out of there on time, and it doesn't sacrifice quality, you should do it!

Old School Cheat Sheets

So if I'm not charting in the room, what do I do? I take good old fashioned hand-written notes – sort of. I have a cheat sheet (see Appendix for your very own copy!) which I take into every visit with me. They are organized by body system and broken into a subjective and objective section; I can easily obtain and record quality information while I'm speaking to the patient, without sacrificing my interactions with the patient. I can easily cross off items that are negatives and circle items that are positives (like crossing off chest pain and circling SOB in a COPD patient with an exacerbation). I have a section for free text notes (things like duration of symptoms, things that help, things that make it worse, details on abnormal findings, etc.), as well as a follow up plan.

When the time comes to chart, I can easily click on or off the things that are in my subjective and objective assessment and write in particular details. I don't have to try to remember things hours later, and I don't have to overly distract myself in the visit by

looking at the screen instead of the patient.

PRODUCTIVE TIP: you can incorporate this

cheat sheet into your time tracking. In the corner, write

the time you go into the exam room, and the time that

you leave. You can take this one step further and write

down the time spent on charting in the same area of

the note and get good quality information regarding

how much time you are spending with the patient

versus how much time you are spending on

administrative tasks. (This could be its own PDSA cycle if

you are feeling really curious or ambitious!)

Shortcuts

Whether you do some of your charting in the

room or leave it all until the visit is over, you are going

to need some shortcuts in your charting life. If your

EMR supports them, set up some dot phrases and smart text (or whatever your EMR calls them) for frequently used phrases and statements (examples: "History significant for" or "If symptoms persist or worsen, return to clinic."). Ask your colleagues for theirs or ask when you have your EMR training; in most organizations, dot phrases, smart text, and templates are shareable but you usually have to know where to look.

An example that I use at the end of every single note (because why would I not say this to every patient?) is *"If symptoms persist, or if any new or concerning symptoms develop, return to clinic."* You will probably find yourself giving the same advice to every patient with an upper respiratory infection, or knee pain, or presenting for their annual physical. You don't have to reinvent the wheel; use a smart phrase and get on with your day. Keep a notebook and jot down things that you notice yourself using frequently in your charting; over time, you will build a good list of fodder for short cuts/phrases.

If your EMR does not have smart text functionality, there are some simple workarounds. Start a Word document with your frequently used text, and keep it open on your desktop while you work. Copy and paste from it into the note, making any slight modifications necessary. (It's still going to be faster than starting from scratch every single time.)

PRODUCTIVE TIP: if you're worried that it will take too long to find the phrase that you are looking for in your Word document, I have a couple of strategies for that (of course!). If you are using Word, then hit "CTRL + F" and the "FIND" window will open; type in a couple of keywords and you'll go straight to what you are looking for. Highlight it, hit "CTRL + C" to copy it, then "CTRL + V" to paste it into the note.

If you want to be even MORE organized, skip Word and go with an Excel spreadsheet instead. Excel works great for this because you have tabs along the bottom, which makes organizing the information even easier; label the tabs for body system (CARDIAC, NEURO, MSK) or type of note (PHYSICAL, PREOP, you name it). Click on the tab, scan the spreadsheet for your phrase (you can use CTRL + F here, too), copy and paste.

Resist the Temptation to Pre-Chart

Another **PRODUCTIVE TIP: don't pre-chart. Ever.** It's a waste of time, and when that patient no-shows, or ends up needing to talk about a completely different issue at their visit, I promise you will be kicking yourself.

It usually seems like a great idea; you see yourself setting everything up to go smoothly for the morning. You look at your visits, open a note, and start poking around in the patient's chart to get some background on the patient for the HPI. Maybe you review some recent lab results, and even pull them into the note if you are feeling ambitious. And then suddenly that six month follow up for the stable diabetic patient turns into a visit about their worsening anxiety since losing their job. *Poof!* All of your pre-charting, out the window. (Think of all the routine lab results you could have checked off of your task list in that time! Actually, don't.)

If you are tempted to try pre-charting, try something more productive instead: pre-order labs. If you see a UTI on your schedule for the afternoon, put in the UA order now. If you have a patient coming in for their annual physical, set up their mammogram, their pap, and any vaccines they may need. If they no-show, it's much less skin off your nose, and if they do show, you have preloaded a little bit of the work and your charting is going to be a little easier.

We Need to Talk – Well, You Do

Are you sitting down? It's time to have the dictation conversation. If you are serious about managing your time and getting out of the clinic at a reasonable time consistently, you must dictate – it's the biggest game-changer out there. No other time-saving tricks can compare.

There are no two ways about it; everyone speaks faster than they type. Dictating will cut your charting time drastically. Through the magic of dictation, I am done for the day consistently at 5:00PM (if not sooner). Combine dictation and templates or the documenting short cuts we talked about and you have some serious time-saving gold.

Like anything, dictation takes practice. Start dictating when you are not stressed and when you will feel comfortable experimenting. You may feel self-conscious when you first start dictating; that is normal. The thought process for dictating is a little different than it is for writing a note, and it will take some time to get used to it. If you feel awkward initially, think about a way to stick with it because the rewards are powerful.

Keep it Simple, Silly

And about your notes? Keep them simple and appropriately succinct. Stick to just the facts; not as short as a haiku*, but you don't need to get into the patient's whole life story, either. Your notes need to capture and reflect what you and the patient discussed in the visit, their report/your observation, *relevant* history, and assessment/plan.

Notes shouldn't take forever to write (of course there are always exceptions) and should be easily digestible for the next person reading it (whether it is you or someone else). Short and sweet and to the point will go a long way toward keeping you on track, on time, and on the way home at an appropriate hour.

Scribes

There is a lot of talk about the use of scribes to help with charting and documentation. If you are not already familiar, scribes are trained to accurately document your visit; when working with you, they will attend your visits and typically complete charting in the room with you and the patient present. In some organizations, assistants are trained to work as scribes; in other organizations, providers are able to select and hire their own scribes (often from an agency); virtual scribes exist, as well. Rules of confidentiality and professionalism apply as they would for any other member of the medical team.

Certainly, having someone ride along and complete your charting for you would be a huge time saver – but at what cost? Consider the literal cost; no scribe is working for free, and even if you have access to a scribe in the form of someone who is already on staff, their assistance to you when scribing takes them away from other duties and represents an expense to the bottom line (if you guessed that those expenses are paid for by you seeing patients, you would be correct).

Consider the patient perspective. Some patients welcome a chaperone at a visit (especially visits where undressing is involved, or any sort of pelvic examination), while others are uncomfortable having another person present. And the point of the scribe is to silently attend to the documentation of the visit; I have met patients who have had scribes present in an encounter, and found the experience to be somewhat creepy. It's understandable.

Another important element to take into consideration is confidentiality. Of course you know that the content of the visit is legally protected and available only on a need-to-know basis. Of course the other members of the team know this, as well, and are held to the same standards. Scribes are no different – but do patients know this? It is understandable for patients to have reservations about having what would appear to be a "third party" present when talking about serious, personal issues.

Have we considered your perspective yet? We should. Are you completely comfortable having another person write your note, with only a cursory review by you before signing it? Will you read every note (how long will that take?), and possibly edit? What will that do to your overall time saved? If you are spending time checking the scribe's work and managing how they work for you, are you really coming out ahead in the time management game?

I have no doubt that using a scribe can be a time saver, and a big one. But I think so much depends on the individual provider-scribe relationship, and the context in which it exists. I suggest giving a considerable amount of thought to the use of a scribe before jumping in with both feet.

I worked with a semi-retired provider who used to write what I think might be the world's shortest notes. A paragraph that (pretty much) encapsulated all the SOAP elements. I used to refer to them as "haiku" — we never understood how the insurance companies would reimburse for such brief notes. But I'll tell you what — that provider was always out of there at 5:00, at the latest!

Chapter 6

During The Visit

Let's talk about how to manage your time during the patient visit. When people ask my secret to consistently running on time, my answer: "Start on time, end on time." It really is that simple, though sometimes it's a convoluted road to get there.

Accessorize

Start with the basics. Put a clock in your exam room where both you and your patient can see it. Make it prominent and easy to read; I'm not talking about a small, travel-sized alarm clock. I'm talking a wall clock of at least 10" in diameter, or a clock radio with a large LED display.

Wear a watch. You may already be in the swing of this, but I have been surprised by how many Nurse Practitioners I have met that seem to shed their wristwatches the minute they pass boards (sometimes these are the same ones who struggle with time management). You might consider setting your watch five minutes ahead (though I would not recommend intentionally setting your clock five minutes ahead – being deceptive with others on purpose is not a good look).

Ordinarily, I don't care for smartwatches, but they can be really helpful when you're learning what the length of a typical visit feels like. Set a vibrating alarm to go off five minutes before the scheduled end of your visit and consider this your "wrap it up"

warning.

Setting Limits

     If you are going to successfully protect your

most precious resource, time, you are going to need to

get comfortable saying no – and enforcing it. Patients

can't have 10 concerns in one visit; rooming staff can't

go on and on and on with patients like it's a social call;

you can't spend a lot of time on idle chit chat with

coworkers. I mean, you *can*, but you're not going to get

out of there on time – sometimes that's an investment

worth making, but that's up to you to decide.

     At the beginning of the visit, set an agenda with

the patient. Saying something like "What would you like

to talk about today?" or the even more specific "What's

on the agenda?" helps to set the tone of the visit and

can take the edge off if you need to tell the patient that you are out of time for today's visit. Let the patient lead but remember that it's your job to manage their expectations - and that includes staying on time. If you can get your rooming staff to be a part of this by using similar language, it will help to set and reinforce this tone from the moment the patient walks into the exam room.

You may need to help patients set limits. There is only so much that can appropriately be covered in one visit, no matter the length. In order to provide safe and effective care, patients deserve an appropriate amount of time for investigation of their concerns. A good rule of thumb is one concern for every 10+/- minutes of visit time. If they want to talk about three unrelated concerns in a 20-minute visit, gently guide them to choose the two most urgent and schedule a return visit for the remaining issue. (If this is not standard operating procedure at your practice, question why.)

If you are getting to the end of the visit and the patient isn't giving any signs of slowing down, don't be afraid to nicely alert the patient that you are nearly out of time for today's visit (this is where having a clock that you both can see can be *very* helpful). Remember, you are the one who is ultimately in charge of what happens in the exam room, and that includes when the visit begins and ends.

A simple switch to make that can speed the visit along is to ask history and physical questions as you do your exam. Sometimes it can be beneficial to let the patient tell you the long version of the story with minimal questioning from you; that's your call. If this is the case, or if your patient arrived significantly late, or the rooming staff took longer than usual to get the patient ready for you, try combining your questions with your exam. You can ask if there is any cough or shortness of breath just before/after the respiratory exam; ask about stool pattern changes after listening to bowel sounds but before palpating; you can ask about hair/nail/skin changes while palpating the thyroid.

Timing Is Everything

Then we have the patients who are late for appointments. In my perfect world, patients arriving after more than 50% of the visit has passed should automatically be rescheduled. For a 20-minute appointment, after 10 minutes I think the patient should be officially "no-showed" and considered to have missed their appointment. There is simply not enough time remaining to investigate their concern appropriately. Beware, though, that this is a double-edged sword; if *you* are not running on time, it becomes much more difficult to ethically enforce a rule like this.

My experience has been that staff will often ask whether you will still see a late-arriving patient. The prevailing policy of your office will likely influence your answer. If the choice is completely yours, be prepared to have to be the bad guy and potentially say no – and be prepared for how this may make you feel.

Consider, briefly, the pros and cons of seeing a late-arriving patient. Sometimes the pros will outweigh the cons, but this is a decision requiring evaluation by the provider. And seeing a late-arriving patient always has the potential to throw off the rest of your morning/afternoon/whole day.

Having a clear rationale for why you are saying no –as discussed here, or what you craft through reflection on your practice – will go a long way to make

you feel more comfortable with where you set your

boundaries and enforcing them when needed. I hope

you never feel guilty for saying no.

Chapter 7

The Flow of Your Day

It's time to focus on the day-to-day stuff above

and beyond charting that can make or break your time

management game.

Back on the Cheat Sheets

PRODUCTIVE TIP: cheat sheets. Now that

you're done with school there's no reason NOT to use

cheat sheets – they're useful for so much! Get a

clipboard or a small notebook and keep it handy. I

prefer a clipboard because I take my notes with a

clipboard (which is stocked with plenty of my charting

cheat sheets, of course). You can add a LOT of stuff to

your clipboard and literally have it at your fingertips at all times. Think of information that you need to reference often but don't necessarily remember off the top of your head. My clipboard has the phone number for the Emergency Department, my NPI and DEA numbers, some mnemonics (SNOOP for headache red flags; CURB-65 for pneumonia), dosing for nicotine patches (why can I never remember it?), the testing/treatment algorithm for tick bites (I live in New England), the extension for IT, the extension for behavioral health, and loads more. Add to it often, and it will become your lifeline and save you time. I've even made copies for colleagues on request!

Break Before You Break

Catch your breath. I don't care what anyone says, you must take a lunch break each day, and ideally not at your desk. Here's the definition of a lunch break

if you need a refresher: a defined period of time during

which you are not working and are not available for work. You eat a MEAL (not a snack), have a drink, use the bathroom maybe? Read the paper, check the weather. Whatever it is, *it ain't work*. And like your phone, you deserve a chance to recharge, even if only briefly.

If you have a private office, close the door, and

put a do not disturb sign on the door (seriously). If you

don't have a private office, go to the cafeteria, medical

staff lounge, outside, to your car, whatever it takes – for

your own sanity, TAKE A BREAK. Even if it's five minutes,

this is part of the self-care of setting and enforcing

boundaries.

Can You Get Rid of It?

Delegate. Be really specific about who can do

what for you (write it down if your team is struggling

with it): rooming staff, secretaries, other staff. And

make sure that they DO the things that you ask them.

Involve their supervisor (if it is someone other than you)

in order to keep this plan on track, if that is warranted.

You are meant to work as a team in service to patients –

and delegation is certainly a part of that (as long as you

are not asking them to do something that is beyond

their professional scope of practice).

Having a sense of how much other staff members are being pulled in other directions is helpful when asking for their assistance – if you have spent time shadowing them (not assuming that you know what they do, but actually seeing it in action), you will have a sense of whether what you are about to ask is reasonable. If it's been a while since you shadowed them, maybe it's time to block off an hour in your schedule to refresh your understanding of the challenges and rewards of their position. Like you, they cannot pour from an empty cup, and if you are going to successfully ask for their help, you need to ask for something that they can reliably and realistically deliver.

Strategize With YOU In Mind

Batch similar tasks. I think of emptying the silverware from the dishwasher to explain this; I take all of the knives out of the basket first, then all of the spoons, then all of the forks. I have literally timed myself taking all of the same items from the basket versus taking things out in a haphazard fashion, and guess what: it's faster when I batch them together.

Check your email twice a day (before starting your morning session, before starting your afternoon session). Do results all together; respond to patient messages all together. It's a different mindset for each, and they don't lend themselves to bouncing back and forth.

If you have admin time, start with the quick wins: result normal labs right away, review referral notes (scan them; you don't have to read every word unless there is a serious concern, or they are hospital/ED discharge notes. If PT is improving the patient with the suspected meniscal tear, that's great, but you probably don't need all the details).

Recognize and seize opportunities when they present themselves. When a patient unexpectedly HAS to use the bathroom before the visit, instead of being annoyed, recognize the little pocket of bonus time you have. Use those five or ten minutes to review labs, close out charts, review a referral/discharge note or two.

Who said that all of your visit time had to be in the exam room? Use five minutes of your 20-minute visit to chart at your desk. On the flip side, sometimes it will be completely unavoidable and a visit will run late; these are the times that you may need to borrow time from other visits. When your abdominal pain patient takes more like 35 minutes instead of 20, you may need to take five minutes from your next three visits to get back on track.

Quick Tasks vs. More Involved Tasks – Know the

Difference

Just as you needed to know what you were

working with in regard to how you were managing your

time, you need to understand what you are working

with in regard to your tasks. When I say "tasks," I'm

talking about all of the things other than visiting with

patients and writing notes about the encounter:

resulting lab work, completing prior authorizations,

engaging with peer review, responding to patient phone

calls, the list goes on and on.

Think of this as understanding your inventory

and learn the difference between quick tasks and more

involved tasks to optimally manage your time. A fast

track to gaining this understanding comes from the time

study worksheets; as you gather data by filling out

those worksheets regularly and completely, you will see

for yourself which tasks are easy and quick for you and which need more of your time.

The difference between quick and more involved tasks can vary depending on the provider and the clinical setting, though there are some broad categorizations that we can make. Typical quick tasks are things like resulting routine labs (*the CMP is normal!*), resulting imaging with no findings (*the ankle ISN'T broken!*), or putting in orders in advance (the mammogram and colonoscopy for your upcoming physicals).

Tasks that tend to be more involved and require more of your time (and focus) are things like charting complex visits, or peer reviews (you are going to be on hold, probably multiple times in one phone call). **PEER REVIEW PRODUCTIVE TIP**: *when is the deadline?* Put some kind of reminder in a place you look frequently (post it on your monitor, reminder on your calendar, or even a flag on your clipboard *PEER REVIEW DUE FRIDAY!*), and pounce on it when you get a chunk of time from a no show or open slot on your schedule.

In a perfect world, you will have staff (ideally, nurses) who will play a role in helping with tasks; most EMRs will have functionality for you to put results notes on the item in question, and forward along to your nurse, who will follow up with the patient. You should have every confidence that once you send these notations along, they are being handled accurately and efficiently. You should not be hearing back from patients requesting results of X, Y, Z that you have already sent along to your nurse.

If this happens more than occasionally, dig a little deeper to understand what may be causing this. Are they short staffed? Were there tech issues, abnormally high call volumes? If no good reason can be found, work with the appropriate person(s) to find a solution.

My Schedule, My Self

You will live and die by your schedule. Your work-life harmony depends on it. Be nice to the people who set your appointments, whether it is secretaries or phone nurses (if you don't know who it is, find out!); even the IT people who adjust the settings for patients to book their own appointments, if your practice does that.

Everyone who is involved in booking appointments for you should know how to book them in a way that won't throw off your schedule before you even get started. You should not have two physicals scheduled back-to-back; you should not have two procedure visits booked back to back; you should not

have patients with suspicion of DVT or acute abdomens

at the end of the day. It would be a tremendous

challenge to successfully run on time if your schedule is

consistently booked inappropriately. I have put

together some booking suggestions (see Appendix) that

you can use with the staff responsible for your

schedule; you will likely need to make some

adjustments to fit the particulars of your practice.

Study your schedule like you were about to take

a test. As much as possible, review your patient

schedule regularly; check the next day's schedule in one

of those one-minute pockets of time, look at the

afternoon's schedule before you go into your next

patient's visit.

Look at your schedule to protect your time; if a

patient has been booked inappropriately (refer to

booking guidelines), notify staff right away to reschedule. Look at your schedule for easy wins that will buy you some time later on or keep you on track – like putting in orders for vaccinations, routine labs, referrals.

Look at your schedule for potential pitfalls – do you have a new patient on your schedule? Check right away for their records from their previous provider so that you can review in advance. Do you have a preop physical? Make sure that any notes from the referring provider (along with any labs or testing that they may want ordered) are available to you BEFORE your visit.

Your time is better spent on other things than hunting down paperwork; there should be other people responsible for this who can make sure the right paperwork gets to you on time – but sometimes that doesn't happen. Regular review of your schedule will spot these problems before they happen – and help to keep you on time.

Best By...

Speaking of orders – if it is an option in your system, put an expiration date on all orders; the specific date of expiration will vary depending on the order itself. Getting a random lab result four months later and having to track down who this patient is and why they had this lab done – and whether it is even still relevant – is a major time waster (me: *"Who is Jane Doe, and why am I getting her CMP?"* Five minutes later, also me: *"Oh, I ordered a CMP for her when I saw her four months ago for lightheadedness after a bout of diarrhea."*).

Here's how I handle it: if it's for a patient with an acute concern, labs expire one week after the visit.

By then, the situation will have probably either resolved or worsened, and in either case the labs will no longer be relevant to our visit (see my CMP example from Jane Doe). If the orders are for a patient having labs or imaging done to accompany a physical, they should ideally be completed prior to the visit so that we can review together but can be done within two weeks of our visit (I explain to patients that this is the best way to "match" my clinical impression in the visit), and screenings (mammograms, colonoscopies, etc.) within three to six months. If orders are for monitoring of a chronic condition (diabetes, cholesterol, thyroid), they should be done a week before the visit, and no later than a week following the visit, for the same reason.

If for some reason it is not an option in your EMR system to put an expiration date on orders, tell the patients that there is a shelf life regarding the relevance of the labs, and do whatever you can to encourage them to abide by appropriate timelines.

And if you do all the right things and still end up with a Jane Doe lab result like I did, when you result the labs, lead your note with the fact that they are no longer clinically relevant, then detail whether they are normal/abnormal and follow up as appropriate.

We've Got a Code "ch"

Get to know your patients — as people, not a collection of diagnoses. For so many reasons, but not the least of which is to manage your time. Some patients will be chatty, some like to throw another concern into the mix when your hand is on the doorknob. Know this, and make note of this.

If there is a place in the chart to leave notes **THAT ONLY YOU CAN VIEW** (this is important!), do that.

If there is not, keep track of these patients in a HIPAA compliant way (maybe keep a list organized by initials and medical record numbers on a sheet of paper, or even use an old school rolodex). In either case, come up with a list of discreet but meaningful codes that will let you know what to expect in the visit before you even go into the room.

I have used "ch" for patients who were a little chatty, and "CH" for patients who were VERY chatty. Lower cased notations mean it's an issue, but upper-cased notations mean it's a major hurdle in the visit. Other notations include "m" for "more" (the patients who always want to add another log on the fire), "KIA" for "know it all" (the silver lining with a KIA patient is that they can be efficient visits – they already knew what was wrong with them), "?" for a patient who asks a million questions. Know what you are walking into with each visit, as much as possible, not just the reason the patient is there; you'll thank yourself when you are strutting out of the office at 5:00PM while everyone else is still in visits.

You will also have patients who are frequently late or habitually no-show. Without judging the whys of their lateness or no-show-ity, it can be helpful to know what to expect (and to maybe be able to count on their habits and use it as a little chunk of bonus time to cross another task off your list!). When patients are late for a visit, I document it in the note, subtly. At the very end of the note, after my footnote about the note having been dictated, I will write something like "5/20", meaning they were five minutes late for a 20-minute visit. I can refer back to that in the future and have a sense of what to expect. You may also find this helpful if you are in a situation where you are running late and need to borrow a few minutes from another visit; if Joe

Late Arrival is on your schedule later in the day, and you

flip back through his last few notes and know he's

always 5-10 minutes late, BOOM! there is your little

pocket of time.

Chart Review

Save time in the visit itself by being prepared. A

judicious but focused review of the chart in advance of

the visit brings you up to speed quickly; has the patient

been seen by other providers since their last visit? What

were those outcomes? (You'll be grateful for succinct

charting by other providers in these moments;

remember to pay it forward.) Any new diagnoses since

their last visit? New medications? Any other notes

relevant to today's visit? Anything on the problem list

that is relevant to today's visit? Skim, skim, skim; this

should take no more than one or two minutes to give

you an overview for the average patient.

Chapter 8

Your EMR Inbox

I had a colleague that was struggling to get a handle on the inbox and tasks and to stay current. I was granted access to the inbox and in my free time (yes, really), I helped out with this massive inbox. (To be completely frank, I actually liked doing it. That's probably a part of why I'm writing this book.)

I was told there were "hundreds" of items, and that was not a joke. But as I dug in, I realized that a lot of these items had at least been opened – though it was not clear whether they had been fully dealt with and could be cleared out, or if they were in limbo for one reason or another. There was so much clutter that it made it hard to tell which end was up, and this certainly contributed to the difficulty in maintaining this inbox.

The first thing that I did was to go after the low hanging fruit. Like I was on a mission, I went through all of the results and looked for easy wins that I could attach a quick note and then dispose of (*A1C is steady, no changes to the plan of care, return to clinic in six months; cervical x-ray within normal limits, no degeneration noted, referred to PT*). This created some breathing room.

Then notes from other disciplines. If it was a note from a routine referral to physical therapy for knee pain, it got a quick scan and then deleted from inbox (copy of course retained in patient chart). If it was a more significant note – a follow up on an oncology referral, or a hospital discharge – that warranted full review by this colleague at earliest convenience. I suggested a plan of doing this during the colleague's weekly admin time.

There were also direct messages from other staff and clinicians. I did not review these for privacy reasons, but I noted that there were a lot of these. Similar to patient messages, I would be cautious about how you are using electronic messaging with your colleagues and your expectations for this sort of communication. Does your office have a policy for these messages – and does the staff follow it? My experience has always been that if there is a message that needs an answer, face to face or phone call is the surest way to get that answer without a ton of back and forth (and potential time wasted).

Next up, patient messages. There were messages from patients that were OLD - like 30 days old. They needed to have eyes on them, but more than anything, they needed to go – they had worn out their

welcome. Anything from a patient that warranted a

discussion with a clinician – that got sent to the staff to

schedule a visit with appropriate level of triage, then

deleted from the mailbox. Again, a little more breathing

room. Anything outdated was treated like old news and

deleted (the patient sent a message on the 1st with

concern for a rash, was seen for that rash on the 8th,

and today was the 22nd? *BYEEE!*). Anything that needed

to be answered by THAT clinician was left in the inbox (I

can't do everything).

This went a long way to getting only the things

that needed to be in the inbox in the inbox and make it

much more manageable when the time came to sit

down and go through this stuff. My advice at this point

was to check it twice a day and respond as appropriate

(knowing that the bulk of the items would need to be

bounced back to other staff for scheduling, follow up, etc.).

Public Service Announcement

This reminds me of the need to set expectations for patient messages. If you are working in a boutique concierge medicine setting and only have a few dozen patients to manage, it is reasonable for patients to communicate with clinicians in this manner – and to expect a return message within a day or two.

Most of us do not work in this sort of setting, and patients should be made aware that messages sent via their electronic chart might not be read for up to one week. No urgent concerns should *ever* be left in a message; these should be addressed in a phone call with a nurse who can triage. By the same token, patients should not expect to have an in-depth back and forth discussion with the clinician via electronic

message. Time is money, and too much of this can turn

into a "free" visit at best, bad clinical outcomes at

worst.

Chapter 9

Know Yourself

We have talked about how to know if your office looks at time management the way you do, how to work with your team, and how to work with your patients. What about you?

Knowing the way that you work and your personal approach to time management is an important piece of the puzzle. Are you easily distracted? Do you like to finish one task completely before moving on to the next? Do you work best in quiet or noisy environments? Do you like to get things done in advance as much as possible or are you energized by the thrill of the deadline? Reflect on these questions and be honest with yourself.

Once you have a sense of your personal approach to time management, you must be **ruthless** in deploying your skills. Identify and remove or manage distractions as much as possible. You have one goal in doing this: keep your time in your control. If there are changes in your work environment (you have new responsibilities, or your panel just had a few hundred people added to it), or if you feel that you need a tune-up, use the time tracker and some PDSA cycles to assess and refine your time management, and influence changes that you need to make to get your time back into balance.

Time Flies

It's true that we don't have control over what happens, only our reaction to it. With this in mind, get a sense of what the length of your visit feels like. Are your visits all 20 minutes? That's basically the length of a sitcom episode on Netflix; pay attention next time you are watching and feel the rhythm of the episode. There is a fairly distinct beginning, middle, and end – and there should be for your visits, too. You could also set a timer while doing another activity – cleaning, reading, walking the dog – and get a sense of what 20 minutes (or the length of your visit) feels like.

Apply this newfound sense of time to your visits; it can take some time to get used to it, but with enough practice you will have a sense for when you have reached the mid-point, and when you are at the winding-down portion of the visit and guide the conversation accordingly.

Would You Rather..?

You are human. Being a provider is just your superpower, it doesn't actually make you superhuman (no matter what administration apparently thinks you are capable of doing). Know your limits and choose your battles. If it is important to you to spend time in the visit chatting with the patient and there is no way that you are going to touch your charts until you are done for the day – there is nothing wrong with that! Recognize that as a decision that *you* made about how you would like to manage your time.

If you are still running on time and not behind, and you want to save all of your charting for your admin time on, say, Thursdays – go for it! But when it comes time to do that charting, remove all distractions and get right down to business. Don't let job creep happen and your job to spill over into your personal life; I have yet to meet the clinician who has let this happen and who is happy with the results.

S.O.S.

And when the need arises – because it does, because we are human as we just discussed – ask for help. This can take a lot of different forms; it can be delegating tasks to staff members, it can be letting patients know that you are actively trying to run on time and ask for their help in keeping you on time, it can be reaching out to leadership to have admin time added to your schedule or the amount increased or to have some visit slots held each day so that you can catch up.

You are responsible for your performance, good or bad, and for recognizing when you need a little (or a lot) of support to get your performance to baseline.

Having a practice of ongoing reflection is a good habit

to get in and can provide plenty of fodder (if needed)

for making an informed case for the support that you

need to be the best professional version of yourself.

Nothing Personal

And here is a relatively easy (on paper, anyway)

strategy for managing your time. No personal stuff at

work (except emergencies). No facebook on your

phone, no texting, no browsing Amazon for a new pair

of Danskos. Doing that is taking time away from the

work you HAVE to do, and if it makes you end up

staying longer – was it really worth it? Just as you have

been advised to prevent having job creep and letting it

spill over into your personal life, you need to prevent

"life creep" and do not let non-important personal

things spill over into your work life.

Chapter 10

Working With A Team

No one works in a vacuum – most people work with other people at least some of the time. Most Nurse Practitioners work with a team of folks – secretaries, medical assistants, techs, nurses, nurse practitioners/ physician assistants/ physicians, administrators. Everyone has a role to play – and everyone should understand their teammates' roles.

I started a job once and met with the practice manager and scheduler (two different people). I asked if there was an organization chart I could review – so that I could get a sense of the different roles on the team and how they related to one another. They just sort of blinked at me when I said this; they had no idea what an "org chart" was – but offered me a phone list. Just a bunch of names and extensions, which didn't really mean anything to me in my first week. This was not a great sign.

Managing – and just as importantly, protecting – your time will be a team effort. The outcome will affect the entire team; when you run late, they run late. When you run late and patients complain – those staff members end up hearing about it. Getting the rest of the team on board with helping to manage and protect your time (as appropriate!) benefits everyone.

Chatty Patty

Just as you need to know what to expect with certain patients, the same is true of rooming staff, who may have the largest direct influence on whether you run on time. Get to know for yourself who is a chatterbox, and who rushes through rooming (I would take feedback on this from other providers and staff with a grain of salt; you don't know all of the nuances of the history behind the feedback, so it's best to determine for yourself). If your office has assistants assigned to specific clinicians, you will get an understanding of this more quickly than if you are in an office that has a round-robin style of assistants and clinicians being paired up. But once you get a sense for this, address any shortcomings or differing expectations it as soon – and as diplomatically – as possible.

How can you handle it in the moment? If the person rooming your patient is taking more than 10 minutes to get it done (this means you have to be paying attention!), you should knock on the door, wait a beat or two before opening it, thanking them, and politely saying that you'll take it from here. If they were taking a long time to reconcile medications but you know that won't be relevant to today's visit, why bother waiting?

If this turns into a trend (more than three times is a trend), a bigger discussion with the pertinent staff and their supervisors should happen to get to the bottom of the issue. Maybe there is a level of support the assistant needs that can help to address the issue; maybe they are doing more than they need to because no one told them any differently. Maybe a quick training would help them with their efficiency. (Maybe they should read this book!)

Keep in mind that you may be the first person to address this with this person. Conversely, you may be the latest in a long line of people to address this. Always approach with an open mind and genuine curiosity. There could be a good reason this is happening; the objective is to identify the root cause and create a plan

(ideally, together) to address the issue.

R.E.S.C.U.E. (to the tune of Aretha Franklin's "Respect")

If you have a good working relationship with

your rooming staff, and you know that you have a

patient coming in that might cause you to run over

unnecessarily (because you looked at your reference

and saw that this patient had the "M" and "?" codes!

You sly fox!), ask for a "rescue knock." Have the staff

knock on the door when the visit is scheduled to end

and ask you to step out of the room; when you return

to the room, let the patient know that you will have to

end for today. You don't need to go into further detail.

Works like a charm, but can be difficult to pull off if you

don't have a great relationship with your rooming staff.

(This is another example of how investing in building

the working relationship with your staff can be extremely beneficial; if you are both facing the same direction, it is a lot easier to address challenges.)

It's a Set Up

Make sure the staff that are rooming your patients know how you want patients set up for different kinds of visits. This will take an investment of time to address in advance, but it's worth it. Doing this will save you time in the long run, will make your work life (and that of your teammates) run more smoothly, and will avoid unnecessary duplication of efforts for a process that can easily be standardized.

Give some thought to the following questions, and think of any others that are unique to your practice that would be helpful to address in advance.

- Do you want all patients undressed and in a gown, or only some of them?

    o If only some – which ones?

    o Is it okay with you if the patient says they'll just "drop their pants" or "lift their shirt" when the time comes?

    o (NOTE: patients getting undressed adds time before you can go into the room! And having staff ask you every time adds time.)

- Do you want the staff to set up for a pap, or is it easier for you to gather the materials yourself when you need them?

    o In that case, do you prefer to have supplies kept in the room when possible – and if so, which ones?

- Do you want the staff to set up for biopsies, suture removals, etc.?
  - What specific items do you want for each of these types of visits?

You may already have all of the answers to these questions and be able to easily put together a nicely typed out list that staff could refer to – but realistically, you will probably know a few of the answers to these questions and have to react to the others as they arise. Plan to revisit this sort of question every few months (or more often if needed) and really cultivate the relationship between you and your rooming staff.

Book 'Em

Make sure that the staff who books your appointments has a good understanding of what is and is not appropriate to book and when (did I mention that there is a booking guideline in the Appendix to get you thinking?). If you are fortunate enough to have different lengths of visits, the shorter ones are best for follow up on one or two simple or well controlled conditions (hypertension, asthma); acute concerns like UTIs; black and white visits such as suture removal; or a patient requesting a referral. Longer visits are best for physicals, follow up for complex patients (with two or more chronic conditions), visits requiring interpreter services, new patient visits.

Things like abdominal pain, chest pain (even in the context of a previous diagnosis), unilateral leg swelling, new shortness of breath should be booked no later than three hours before the end of the day – though consideration should always be given to whether these patients are even appropriate for your clinical setting or whether they should be seen in an

urgent or emergent setting, regardless of time.

Role Models

Look around: is there someone that you work

with, or know, who is a good role model for time

management? How do they stay on track? What do

they do? What do they avoid? Ask them for tips or to

pick their brain (but never ask them on the fly – set up a

dedicated time!).

Give It Away

Look critically at what and how you do what you

do. What *has* to be done by you? What can you give

away? Can assistants tee up routine orders so that you

just sign them? Can secretaries automatically hand out

PHQ9/GAD7 screeners to patients coming in for

depression/anxiety appointments?

Chapter 11

Developing A Reflective Practice

One of the most important things that I learned in school was the importance of a reflective practice. We were required to reflect weekly on what we experienced in our clinical rotations, how that affected us, and what we learned from it (above and beyond the clinical component). We met weekly and shared these written reflections with a professor as well as a small group of fellow students. It was a great way to build a practice self-care as budding clinicians, as well as to cultivate being more aware during our clinical experiences. Sharing these reflections with others provided opportunity to both give and receive support and to learn from the experiences of others. It was certainly one of the most impactful elements of my Nurse Practitioner training.

I was surprised once I entered practice to find how many fellow clinicians did not have a similar opportunity, and how much I think they could have benefitted from taking some time on a regular basis to reflect on how things have been going and give some thought to how they want to grow as clinicians. But you are reading this, so you have already taken the first step toward investing in yourself as a clinician and growing your practice with intention. That really is half the battle.

I learned a process called naikan reflection that has helped me immensely in maintaining a reflective practice as a Nurse Practitioner. The word "naikan" loosely translates to looking inside or viewing oneself with the mind's eye. Naikan reflection was developed in the 1940s by Ishin Yoshimoto as a technique for stepping back and reflecting on the life that you are living; its power in showing the connections and relationships between parties makes it a very good method for clinicians, as relationships are the foundation of everything that we do with patients, colleagues, and team mates.

I have found this to be a very simple but effective method for self-reflection, and a potent combination that is relatively easy to deploy as an often *very* busy clinician. It is equally effective as a regular practice (for example, completed weekly), or focused on a specific event or episode.

Completing regular Naikan reflections, and keeping them together, provides a great means for understanding and appreciating exactly how far you have come, as well as where you are going. This is especially important in that first year of practice when you frequently feel overwhelmed or like you don't know anything. This technique can also be very useful when starting a new position (when you once again feel like you don't know anything), or when your job has changed and you suddenly have new responsibilities.

How do you do it? The process is built on three remarkably simple questions:

- What have I received from _____ ?
- What have I given to _____ ?
- What troubles and difficulties have I caused _____ ?

Performing naikan reflection daily may be unrealistic for busy clinicians. Instead, I would suggest setting aside some time each week – either at the end of the week or as you prepare to begin a new week. Plan on a 20–30-minute block of time. Go to a quiet place, where you are able to relax and will not be interrupted. Get a notebook, and a writing instrument that you love; you will complete these reflections in writing, by hand. We are often more authentic and less likely to edit our thoughts when writing by hand, especially if it is in a location (like a notebook) that is meant only for our eyes.

Once you have chosen your location and gathered your materials, reflect on the three questions, in relation to the previous work week. What have you received from your practice in the past week? While there are no right or wrong answers, there are no answers that are too small or seemingly insignificant to be included. Maybe it was a pay week, and you received a sense of security from being compensated. Maybe you had a remarkably busy schedule that you didn't think you would be able to handle, but you found that it went more smoothly than expected. Maybe you had some very challenging patients and you received an opportunity to learn new skills for relating to patients (or things to watch out for next time).

What have you given to your practice in the past week? You brought your compassion and knowledge to patients. You were able to promote someone's health, or maybe alleviate someone else's suffering. Did you help a patient by giving them an answer to a question that was difficult for them to ask? Did you cover for a colleague? Did you identify a problem and propose a solution?

What troubles and difficulties have I caused my practice? This is typically the most challenging question in this simple exercise; it requires you to think about how any (or all) of your actions impacted those around you, for better or worse. It's an important part of the reflective process, because if we don't recognize and acknowledge the things that we did that made difficulty for others, then we are acting as though we are entitled to simply receive everything that we want without trouble. You probably already know that is unrealistic, but to actively embody recognizing that fact takes practice, skill, and humility.

Were you short with rooming staff, causing them stress? Did you run late all week, making colleagues' jobs more difficult and stressing out patients who were waiting for you? Were you sick? (Don't feel guilty if you were but recognize how that impacted those around you.) Dig deep and work to recognize the impact of your actions on your surroundings. This step will get easier once you have been practicing this method for a while, but the beauty of the challenge inherent in this question is that it makes you focus on the impact of your actions on those around you.

As we discuss elsewhere in this book, understanding how the pieces of the team fit together (no matter how big or small the team may be) is essential. I firmly believe that medicine is a relationship business at its core; having superior medical knowledge is an important and non-negotiable element of the business, but does not excuse ignoring the relationship aspect of the work we do as providers.

Building a reflective practice will serve you, the rest of the team, and your patients. A reflective practice will deepen your understanding of how your actions positively or negatively impact others just as much as how their actions positively or negatively impact you. Being skilled in this way will elevate your practice and make you a more thoughtful, evolved, deliberate

colleague and clinician. (*cough* ***ROCKSTAR!*** *cough*)

Conclusion

Whew, you made it all the way through – congratulations!

I hope that in the process, you have developed a deeper knowledge about yourself, how you practice, and your relationship with time. I hope that you have found some pearls that you can use right away, and that some seeds have been planted that will eventually develop into pearls of your own.

Revisit these pages as needed when you need to refresh your approach to time management, when you begin to feel overwhelmed by the clinician life, or when you have an expansion in your responsibilities.

Time management is not a one size fits all discipline, and it's not a one-time assessment. It's a living, breathing, evolving discipline that – kind of like a

garden – requires attention, fertilization, and pruning.

What works for you now may not work for you at your

next job, and that's okay. If you have the basic tools,

you can apply them to a variety of situations (like

gardening – see what I did there?), and get results. And

you've got the tools now. Go use them!

APPENDIX

For downloadable full page worksheets, visit
ourcoach.online/blank-page

The World's Most Productive Nurse Practitioner – Time Tracker	
DAY:	
DATE:	**ACTIVITY**
00:00 – 00:30	
00:30 – 01:00	
01:00 – 01:30	
01:30 – 02:00	
02:00 – 02:30	
02:30 – 03:00	
03:00 – 03:30	
03:30 – 04:00	
04:00 – 04:30	
04:30 – 05:00	
05:00 – 05:30	
05:30 – 06:00	
06:00 – 06:30	
06:30 – 07:00	
07:00 – 07:30	
07:30 – 08:00	
08:00 – 08:30	
08:30 – 09:00	
09:00 – 09:30	
09:30 – 10:00	
10:00 – 10:30	
10:30 – 11:00	
11:00 – 11:30	
11:30 – 12:00	
NOTES	

The World's Most Productive Nurse Practitioner – Time Tracker	
DAY:	
DATE:	**ACTIVITY**
12:00 – 12:30	
12:30 – 13:00	
13:00 – 13:30	
13:30 – 14:00	
14:00 – 14:30	
14:30 – 15:00	
15:00 – 15:30	
15:30 – 16:00	
16:00 – 16:30	
16:30 – 17:00	
17:00 – 17:30	
17:30 – 18:00	
18:00 – 18:30	
18:30 – 19:00	
19:00 – 19:30	
19:30 – 20:00	
20:00 – 20:30	
20:30 – 21:00	
21:00 – 21:30	
21:30 – 22:00	
22:00 – 22:30	
22:30 – 23:00	
23:00 – 23:30	
23:30 – 24:00	
NOTES	

Booking

Some guidelines related to booking appointments. Use these as a starting point to establish what your team should and should not do when booking appointments for you

- **DO NOT BOOK LESS THAN 3 HOURS BEFORE END OF DAY/SHIFT:**
    - abdominal pain
    - suspicion of DVT (unilateral leg swelling, redness, warmth, pain/tenderness, patient not currently anticoagulated)
    - new onset shortness of breath (even if patient has previous diagnosis of asthma/COPD)
    - acute or acute on chronic chest pain

- if active chest pain, send patient immediately to emergency department
- if exertional chest pain, patient to present immediately to emergency department
- if acute on chronic chest pain, can be a toss up - but lean in the direction of emergency department
  - new onset of unilateral numbness, tingling, weakness or fatigue: always send to emergency department
- Do not book two procedure visits back to back
  - examples: pap, vaginal swab, biopsy, IUD removal/insert, joint injection

- Do not book two visits requiring interpreter services back to back

- Do not book two physicals back to back

- Do not book two new patient visits back to back

- First appointment of morning and afternoon should be acute visits (do not book these appointments more than 12 hours in advance)

- Follow up visits for chronic conditions (diabetes, asthma/COPD, anxiety/depression, hypertension):
  - no more than two concerns can adequately be addressed per visit
  - if more than two concerns to be covered, book in double slot/longer slot, or book two appointments

- New patient visits should be double length or 45 minutes

- Preop visits should not be booked unless

  paperwork from surgeon is available (indicating

  any labs or other testing they require)

Suggested Scripts For Combining Exam and History and Physical

- While assessing EOM / PERRLA / ears / palpating thyroid:
  - "Any headaches on a regular basis? More than 3x/month?"
  - "Any changes to hair, skin, nails?"
- Immediately before auscultating lungs:
  - "Any new cough or shortness of breath?"
  - "Any chest pain?"
- Immediately before beginning abdominal exam (while lifting shirt/gown):
  - "Any changes to your bowel pattern?"
  - "Any heartburn on a regular basis?"
  - "Pain or difficulty with urination?"

- Immediately before beginning clinical breast exam (while lifting shirt/gown):
  - "Do you do self exams?"
  - "Have you noticed any changes?"
- While having patient get off table and touch toes:
  - "Any new aches and pains? Are they predictable?"
- During pap:
  - "Any discomfort or pain with intercourse?"

Charting Shortcuts

Use these as a starting point to customize your notes or templates; change the negatives to positive as needed, delete the things you don't need, and watch your charting time get cut back drastically.

Subjective

Constitutional

Patient presents with concern for _____. Denies: changes in appetite, fever, chills, sweats, weight change or fatigue. History significant for: _____.

Head

Patient denies any trauma, new lumps or masses, tenderness, rash or lesions.

Eyes

Patient denies vision changes (blur, diplopia), itch or discharge, excessive tearing or dryness. No photophobia. No history of cataracts, glaucoma. Patient does not wear glasses or contact lenses. Last eye exam: _____.

Ears, Nose, Throat

Patient denies hearing change, ear pain, discharge, vertigo; no suspicion of ear infection. Patient denies epistaxis, nasal and sinus congestion. Patient denies bleeding or swelling of gums, oral pain, sore throat, or subjective voice change. Last dental exam: _____.

Patient denies neck pain, lumps, swelling, or difficulty swallowing.

Cardiac

Patient denies chest pain, pressure, dizziness, nausea, SOB or weakness with exertion, palpitations. No numbness or tingling of extremities. No subjective edema, coldness of extremities, delayed wound healing. No history of murmurs, hypertension, MI.

Respiratory

Patient denies wheezing, shortness of breath, cough, hemoptysis. No history of asthma, COPD, bronchitis, pneumonia.

Gastrointestinal

Patient denies abdominal pain, change in bowel habits,

constipation, diarrhea, nausea, vomiting, black/bloody

or otherwise discolored stools. Patient denies

dysphagia, heartburn. No previous history of hepatitis,

gallstones, hemorrhoids.

Genitourinary

Patient denies difficult, burning, or pain with urination;

denies nocturia, polyuria, hematuria. Patient denies

urinary incontinence, suspicion of infection. No history

of kidney or bladder stones.

Genital

Patient denies discharge, genital sores, pain, or masses.

Patient is sexually active; denies dyspareunia. Patient

uses contraception: _____. No history of sexually

transmitted infection; no new sexual partners or recent

unprotected intercourse. Last menstrual period: _____.

Last OB/GYN exam: _____.

Musculoskeletal

Patient denies redness, swelling, warmth, pain,

discomfort, limitations to range of motion, muscle

cramps. No history of arthritis, fractures, sprains, joint

replacement. Patient denies AM/PM joint stiffness.

Skin

Patient denies rash, pruritis, jaundice, bruising, lesions,

delayed wound healing. Patient denies changes in hair,

nails; no change to existing nevi. No history of skin

cancer.

Breasts

Patient denies lumps, pain, nipple discharge, change in skin texture. Last mammogram: _____. Last clinical breast exam: _____. Patient performs self breast exams.

Neuro

Patient denies frequent or new headaches, seizures, vertigo. Patient denies subjective memory, gait, speech or coordination changes.

Psych

Patient denies suicidal, homicidal ideation. Patient denies depression, anxiety, change in sleep pattern. Patient denies history of substance or alcohol abuse. No previous mental health diagnoses. No history of mental or physical abuse.

Endocrine

Patient denies polydipsia, polyuria, polyphagia. No subjective heat or cold intolerance, or significant changes in energy level. Patient denies changes in hair, nails, skin.

Heme/Lymph

Patient denies significant bruising, lymphadenopathy, axillary or groin tenderness. No history of blood disorders, transfusions, anemia, anticoagulation.

Allergy/Immunology

Patient denies seasonal, food, medication allergies. Patient denies known immune disorders.

Objective

General

Patient is well appearing, well nourished, alert and oriented x3. Patient displays normal mood, affect.

Neurological

Cranial nerves intact and symmetrical. EOM intact. PERRLA. Reflexes intact, normal, and symmetrical (SPECIFY LOCATION TESTED; SPECIFY #/5). Strength equal and symmetrical in all four extremities. Sensation intact. Hearing intact to spoken words at conversational volume.

Dermatological

Skin color and turgor normal for ethnicity, age. No obvious rashes, scaling, broken skin, unusual bruising, prominent lesions noted. No discoloration or

deformities of nails. Texture and distribution of hair

within normal limits.

Head, Eyes, Ears, Nose, Throat

Head is normocephalic, atraumatic, with no visible or

palpable masses noted. No obvious depressions,

scarring noted. Visual acuity grossly intact (with

glasses/contacts), extraocular movements grossly

intact, fields of vision grossly intact; conjugate gaze.

Conjunctiva clear bilaterally; no discharge or redness

present. PERRLA. Funduscopic exam within normal

limits bilaterally. No exudate, no hemorrhage noted.

External auditory canals patent bilaterally, no excessive

cerumen noted; tympanic membranes translucent and

mobile bilaterally. No mid-ear effusion noted. Hearing

grossly intact to spoken words at conversational

volume. No lesions or mucosal inflammation noted in bilateral nares; septum grossly midline. No swelling of turbinates noted; no obvious discharge. No frontal or maxillary sinus tenderness to palpation. Oropharynx within normal limits; free of lesions, erythema, obvious/significant caries or abnormal dentition, obvious gingival inflammation; mucous membranes moist. No tonsillar hypertrophy or exudate noted. Neck is supple with grossly normal ROM. No bruit, adenopathy, JVD noted. No obvious hypertrophy or tenderness of thyroid to palpation. Non-nodular.

Cardiac

Regular rate and rhythm; S1, S2 present. No murmur, rub, click, gallop noted. No PMI displacement noted. Pulses present and symmetrical in bilateral extremities. No visible swelling of extremities, no pitting edema.

Respiratory

Lungs clear to auscultation in all fields bilaterally. No inspiratory or expiratory wheezes noted. No rales, crackles, rhonchi noted on auscultation. Patient speaks in full, complete sentences without limitation.

Breast

Breasts are symmetrical. No dimples, retractions, skin changes noted. No masses appreciated. No nipple abnormalities or discharge on exam. No tenderness to palpation. Axillary and clavicular nodes nontender, nonrigid, not enlarged or fixed.

Abdominal

Bowel sounds present in all four quadrants. No tenderness to palpation. No masses appreciated; no organomegaly noted. No hernia. Patient ascends/descends exam table without limitation or significant effort.

Rectal

Sphincter tone normal. No internal or external hemorrhoids noted. No palpable masses. No blood noted in rectal vault.

Gynecological

Patient in supine position. Vulva and vagina normal; no erythema, abnormal discharge, lesions. Cervix normal, nondilated; no discharge, no lesions, not friable, no cervical motion tenderness. No obvious prolapse of bladder or uterus. No adnexal masses or tenderness to palpation. Rectal tone normal; no hemorrhoids appreciated.

Genitourinary

Penis is circumcised and free of lesions. Urethra midline; no discharge, no erythema. Cremasteric reflex present bilaterally; no swelling, varicocele, hydrocele noted. Digital rectal exam within normal limits; prostate is non-tender, non-nodular. No inguinal hernia.

Musculoskeletal

No obvious misalignment, asymmetry, defects, or obvious swelling noted. No crepitation or effusion appreciated on exam; no tenderness in joints on palpation. Gait and ROM grossly within normal limits; normal muscle bulk and tone. Reflexes symmetrical bilaterally (#/5, location) and grossly within normal limits; strength equal bilaterally in upper and lower extremities.

Back

No abnormal curvature or tenderness noted; ROM grossly within normal limits. No CVA tenderness.

Extremities

No amputations or deformities present. No significant varicosities, cyanosis, or edema; peripheral pulses present and symmetrical bilaterally.

Psych

Alert and oriented to person, place, time. Intact recent and remote memory; judgment, insight, and affect grossly within normal limits. No anxiety, depression, suicidal ideation or homicidal ideation.

Foot

Pulses present bilaterally in dorsalis pedis, posterior tibialis locations. No abnormally thickened nails, broken skin, significant dry skin, significant erythema, calluses present. Monofilament test positive in all locations.

PDSA Worksheet

Date	
Process being studied (describe in detail)	
Which PDSA cycle is this?	1 2 3 4 5 other:
PLAN	
Identify the improvement that you are seeking. What are the goals? What are your predictions? What data should be gathered as part of this study? Are there any tools that are needed in	

order to execute the plan?	
DO	
Implement plan and begin analysis of results. Were there any barriers or knowledge gaps that impeded or limited the execution of the plan? List the data gathered. List any problems encountered.	
STUDY	
Reflect on results. How did the process go? Were there any surprises, good or bad? How did the data	

gathered compare to the predictions in the first step?	
ACT	
Update your approach. What changes will you make to the process moving forward? Begin next cycle.	

Naikan Reflection Worksheet

To be completed weekly, for review at the end of the

week or in preparation for a new week. Write answers

out by hand, as you are less likely to edit your thoughts

when writing by hand (as compared to typing), which

will increase the benefits of your reflective practice. Use

additional paper as necessary.

What have I received from my practice this week?

What have I given to my practice this week?

What troubles or difficulties have I caused my practice?

Last Name or ID#:   Date of visit:
Reason for visit: Age: Gender:

CONST. Δ appetite, energy, wt / fever / chills / sweats / fatigue
HEAD   trauma / mass / tenderness / rash / lesions
EYES visionΔ / itch / d/c / tears / dry / ctrcts / glau / glass, tacts
ENT hearing Δ / pain / d/c / vertigo / ? infection // epistaxis /
congestion // bleeding, swelling gums / pain / sore throat /
voice Δ // neck pain / lumps / swelling / difficulty swallowing
CARDIAC pain / pressure / dizzy / N / orthopnea / edema /
palp / weak w exertion / hx murmurs / hx MI / HTN / HF / numb
/ tingle / cold extrem / slow wound healing
RESP wheeze / SOB / cough / asthma / bronch / COPD
GI abd pain / Δ in bowels / constipation / diarrhea / N V /
hepatitis / g-stones / dysphagia / reflux / hemorrhoids / black,
bloody stools
GU burn / pain / noct- poly- hematuria / incont / infect / stones
GENITAL   DC / sores / pain / masses / last pap _____ /
sexually active Y N / dyspareunia / LMP   / contraception
MSK   redness / swelling / warmth / pain / +/- ROM / arthritis
/ musc cramps / frac / sprains / joint repl / stiffness: AM PM
SKIN   rash / pruritis / jaundice / bruising / hx skin ca / mole Δ
/ Δ in hair, nails / lesions / slow wound healing
BREASTS lumps / pain / dc / last mammo   / self exams YN
NEURO HA / sz / vertigo / memory Δ / gait Δ / speech / coord
PSYCH suicidal / homicidal / depression / anxiety / Δ in sleep
pattern / substance, ETOH abuse
ENDO   polydip, polyuria / heat, cold intol / Δ hair/nails/energy
HEM/LYMPH   anemia / bruising / hx transfusions / blood
disorder / lymphadenopathy / axillary, groin tender
ALLX/IMMUN   season allx / food allx / med allx / imm dis.

SOCIAL HX   # in household _____ / lives with
SP/BF/GF/SO / children __ / tobacco Y/N #pk _____ / sexual
activity Y/N / etoh, other substances Y/N / occupation:
FAM HX   ca / HTN / MI / CAD / stroke / hyperlipid /
DM2 / Alzheimer's / depression / osteoporosis / other:

NOTES:

BP:
HR:
T:
O2%:
HT:
WT:
BMI:
PAIN:

GENERAL well appearing / well nourished / a&o x 3 / normal mood, affect **NEURO** intact / abn / DTR

SKIN + NAILS turgor / rash, bruising, lesions / texture, distribution of hair / nails: abn color, deform

HEENT **HEAD** normocephalic / atraumatic / visible, palp masses / depressions / scarring

EYES acuity intact / conjunctiva clear / EOM intact / PERRLA / fundi - normal discs and vessels / icterus / exudate / hemorrhage

EARS EACs clear / TM translucent, mobile / landmarks abnormal / hearing diminished

NOSE lesions / mucosal inflamm / septum, turbinates abn

MOUTH mucous memb dry / mucosal lesions / poor dentition / caries / gingival inflamm

PHARYNX mucosa inflamm / tons hypertrophy, exudate

NECK supple / ROM normal / lesion / bruit / adenopathy / thyroid enlarged, tender / mass

CARDIAC regular rate, rhythm / S1, S2 / murmur / gallop / click / rub / PMI dsplcmnt

RESP clear all fields / wheezes (insp) (exp) / rales / crackles

ABDOMEN BSx4 / tender / organomegaly / mass / hernia

RECTAL abn tone / hemorrhoids (int/ext) / palp mass

BACK abn curvature / tenderness / CVAT / Δ ROM

EXTREMITIES ampu / deformity / edema / varicos / + pulses

MSK abn gait / asymmetry / crepitation / defect / tender / mass / effusion / Δ ROM / instability / atrophy / abn strength, tone in head, neck, spine, ribs, pelvis, UE, LE / patho reflexes

PSYCH A&O x3 / +recent/remote memory / insight / affect

BREAST nipple abn / masses / tenderness / axillary, clavicular adenopathy

GYN/GU lesions / d/c / uterus, adnexa tenderness / CMT // circumcised / penile lesions / urethra normal location, no d/c / testes normal / + cremasteric reflex

FEET +pulses / monofilament + / nails abn / dry, broken skin / callus /

LABS CBC / CMP / lipids / TSH / microalbumin / A1C / UA, culture / PSA / iron studies / other:

DIAGNOSTICS XR / MRI / CT / US / cardiac / other

REFERRALS **F/U** ___ wk ___ mo

CPSIA information can be obtained
at www.ICGtesting.com
Printed in the USA
LVHW050825280523
748253LV00007B/959